SO-AJX-632

SCHOLASTIC

Do The Math™

Created by
Marilyn Burns

✕ Multiplication Ⓐ

Basic Concepts

· ·

WorkSpace

Cover photo: © Bob Stefko/Getty Images; Illustrations pp.15–19; 55: Frank Montagna © Scholastic Inc.

Copyright © 2008 by Scholastic Inc.

All rights reserved.   Published by Scholastic Inc.   Printed in the U.S.A.

ISBN 978-0-545-00693-4

SCHOLASTIC, DO THE MATH, and associated logos and designs are trademarks and/or registered trademarks of Scholastic Inc.

1   2   3   4   5   6   7   8   9   10   40   16   15   14   13   12   11   10   09   08   07

Circles and Stars Practice Turns

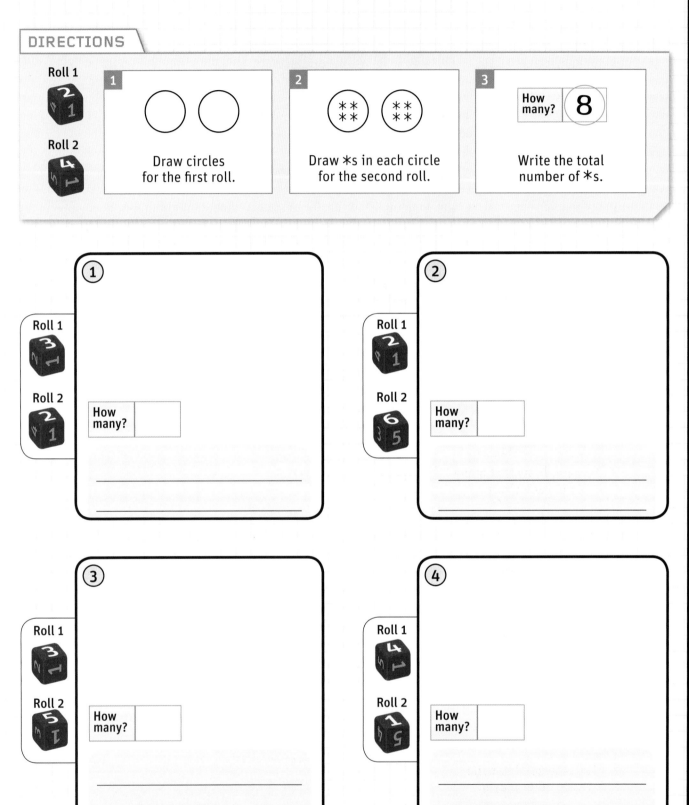

DIRECTIONS

Roll 1

Roll 2

1 Draw circles for the first roll.

2 Draw ✳s in each circle for the second roll.

3 How many? **8** Write the total number of ✳s.

1

Roll 1

Roll 2

How many?

2

Roll 1

Roll 2

How many?

3

Roll 1

Roll 2

How many?

4

Roll 1

Roll 2

How many?

Home Note: Your child draws equal groups of stars and finds the total number of stars.

Game Rules for Circles and Stars

HOW TO PLAY

What you need

- number cube (1–6)
- *WorkSpace* pages 3 and 4 or blank paper
- pencil

➤ **Players take turns. Each turn has four steps.**

1 Roll. Draw that many circles.

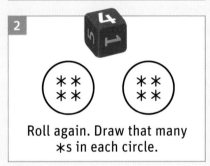

2 Roll again. Draw that many ✳s in each circle.

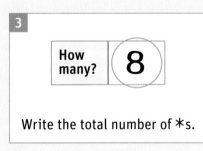

3

| How many? | 8 |

Write the total number of ✳s.

4 Hand the number cube to the other player.

➤ **The winner is the player who gets the most ✳s in eight turns.**

Home Note: Your child learns a multiplication game.

Lesson 1

3

Circles and Stars Multiplication Game

➤ Players take turns. Each turn has four steps.

1

Roll. Draw that many circles.

2

Roll again. Draw that many ✱s in each circle.

3

How many? | 8

Write the total number of ✱s.

4

Hand the number cube to the other player.

➤ The winner is the player who gets the most ✱s in eight turns.

①

How many?

_____

_____

②

How many?

_____

_____

③

How many?

_____

_____

④

How many?

_____

_____

⑤

How
many?

_____

_____

⑥

How
many?

_____

_____

⑦

How
many?

_____

_____

⑧

How
many?

_____

_____

Total

Home Note: Your child practices writing
and solving multiplication equations.

Circles and Stars Equations

DIRECTIONS

1

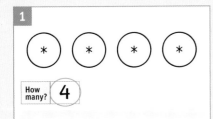

How many? ④

_____

_____

Write how many *s in all.

2

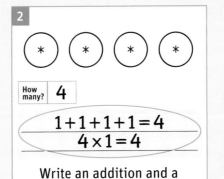

How many? 4

$$1+1+1+1=4$$
$$4 \times 1 = 4$$

Write an addition and a multiplication equation.

①

How many? [ ]

_____

_____

②

How many? [ ]

_____

_____

③

How many? [ ]

_____

_____

④

How many? [ ]

_____

_____

🏠 **Home Note:** Your child writes addition and multiplication equations for equal groups.

Multiplication Equations

DIRECTIONS

➤ Write a multiplication equation for each card.

 $6 \times 5 = 30$

1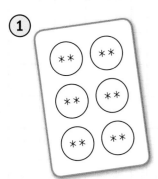

_____

2

_____

3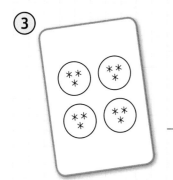

_____

4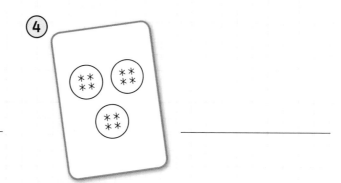

_____

5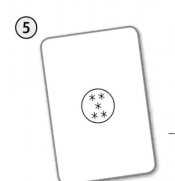

_____

6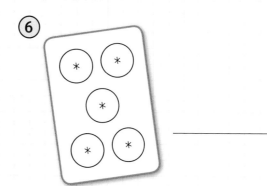

_____

🏠 **Home Note:** Your child writes the multiplication equation for equal groups.

Circles and Stars

DIRECTIONS

➤ Draw circles and *s.

➤ Write how many *s in all.

➤ Write an addition equation and a multiplication equation.

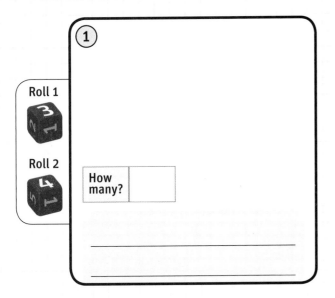

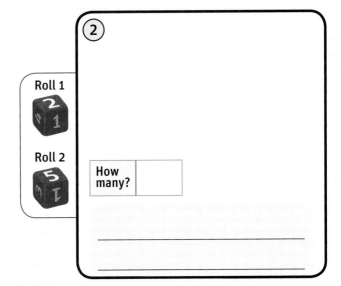

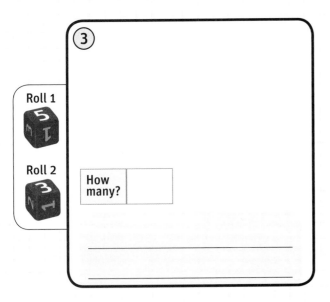

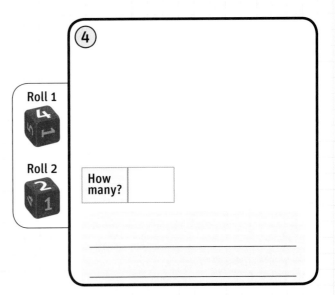

Lesson 5

Home Note: Your child draws equal groups and then writes addition and multiplication equations for the groups.

Show What You Know

➤ Write how many ✳s in all.

➤ Write an addition equation and a multiplication equation.

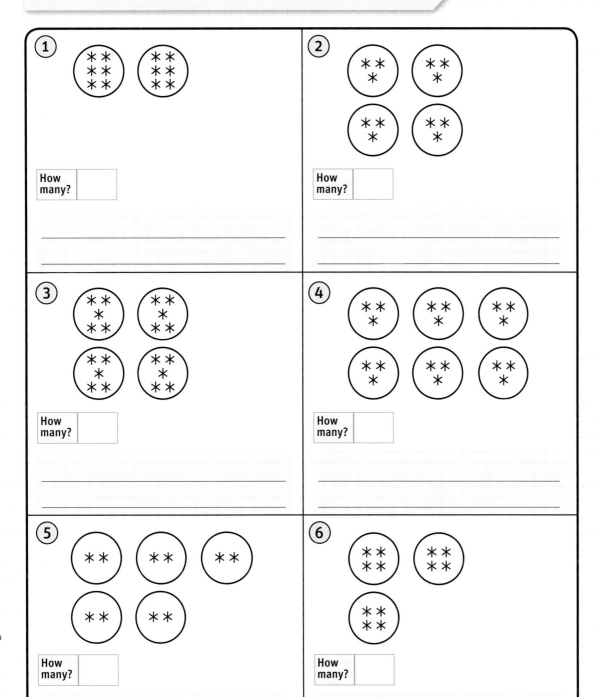

1 How many? ☐

2 How many? ☐

3 How many? ☐

4 How many? ☐

5 How many? ☐

6 How many? ☐

🏠 **Home Note:** Your child writes addition and multiplication equations for equal groups.

Game Rules for Circles and Stars Capture

What you need

- *Circles and Stars Capture* cards, 9 cards per player
- *WorkSpace* pages 11 and 12 or blank paper
- pencil

➤ **Each turn has three steps.**

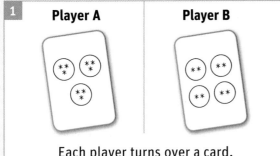

1 | **Player A** | **Player B**

Each player turns over a card.

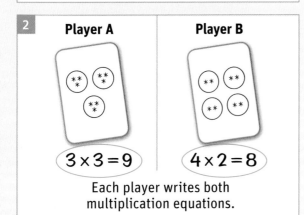

2 | **Player A** | **Player B**

$3 \times 3 = 9$ $4 \times 2 = 8$

Each player writes both
multiplication equations.

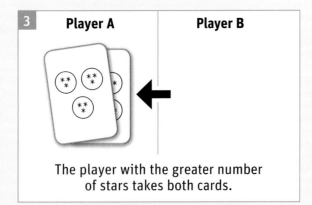

3 | **Player A** | **Player B**

The player with the greater number
of stars takes both cards.

➤ **When all the cards have been played, the winner
is the player who has the most cards.**

Home Note: Your child learns a multiplication game.

Circles and Stars Capture

HOW TO PLAY

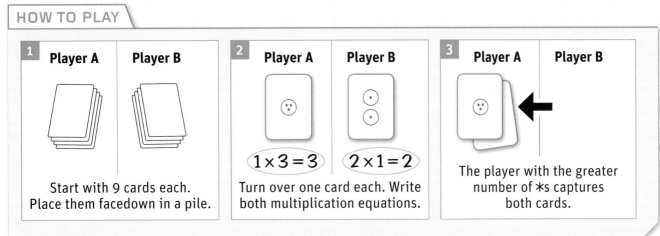

1. **Player A** | **Player B**
Start with 9 cards each. Place them facedown in a pile.

2. **Player A** | **Player B**
$1 \times 3 = 3$ $2 \times 1 = 2$
Turn over one card each. Write both multiplication equations.

3. **Player A** | **Player B**
The player with the greater number of *s captures both cards.

Player A	Player B

Home Note: Your child practices writing and solving multiplication equations.

Lesson 5

11

Circles and Stars Capture

HOW TO PLAY

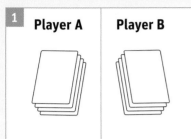

1 | Player A | Player B

Start with 9 cards each.
Place them facedown in a pile.

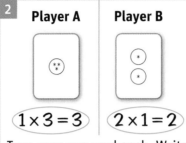

2 | Player A | Player B

$1 \times 3 = 3$ $2 \times 1 = 2$

Turn over one card each. Write both multiplication equations.

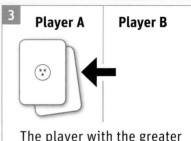

3 | Player A | Player B

The player with the greater number of ✱s captures both cards.

Player A	Player B

Home Note: Your child practices writing and solving multiplication equations.

Things That Come in Groups

DIRECTIONS

➤ Write more things on the lists.

Groups of 2
socks
twins
eyes
slices of bread in sandwiches

Groups of 3
tennis balls in cans
triplets
sides on triangles

Home Note: Your child writes things that come in groups to prepare for writing multiplication word problems.

Things That Come in Groups

➤ Write more things on the lists.

Groups of 4
dog legs
table legs
sides on squares

Groups of 5
fingers on hands
points on stars

Groups of 6	
insect legs	

Home Note: Your child writes things that come in groups to prepare for writing multiplication word problems.

Equal Group Problems

How many bug legs?

1

$6 + 6 + 6 + 6 = 24$

Write the addition equation.

2

$6 + 6 + 6 + 6 = 24$

$4 \times 6 = 24$

Write the multiplication equation.

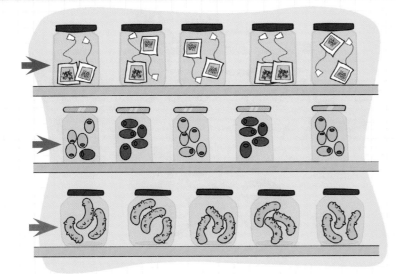

➤ ① **How many teabags?**

_____

_____

➤ ② **How many olives?**

_____

_____

➤ ③ **How many pickles?**

_____

_____

Home Note: Your child writes addition and multiplication equations to match pictures.

Lesson 8

15

Equal Group Problems

➤ Write the addition equation.
➤ Write the multiplication equation in numbers and in words.

1 How many wheels?

_____

_____

2 How many legs?

_____

_____

3 How many balls of yarn?

_____

_____

 Home Note: Your child writes addition and multiplication equations to match a picture.

Equal Rows Problems

DIRECTIONS

➤ Write the addition equation.

➤ Write the multiplication equation.

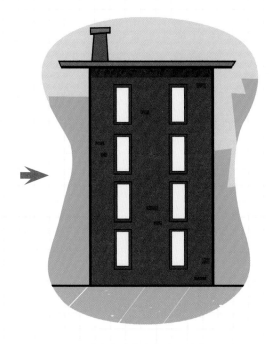

➤ ① **How many windows?**

_____

_____

➤ ② **How many muffins?**

_____

_____

➤ ③ **How many bagels?**

_____

_____

Home Note: Your child writes addition and
multiplication equations to match pictures.

Show What You Know

DIRECTIONS

➤ Write the addition equation.
➤ Write the multiplication equation.

(1) How many plants?

_____

_____

(2) How many knitting needles?

_____

_____

Home Note: Your child writes addition and multiplication equations to match equal groups and rows in pictures.

Show What You Know

DIRECTIONS

➤ Write the addition equation.
➤ Write the multiplication equation in numbers and in words.

➡ ① **How many sheep eyes?**

_____

_____

➡ ② **How many pictures?**

_____

_____

Home Note: Your child writes addition and multiplication equations to match equal groups and rows in pictures.

A Tricycle Problem

DIRECTIONS

1

There are 5 bikes.

Each has 2 wheels.

How many wheels are there in all?

Read the word problem.

2

$5 \times 2 = \boxed{}$

Write the multiplication equation.

3

2, 4, 6, 8, 10

Show your figuring.

4

$5 \times 2 = \boxed{10}$

Write the answer.

1 EQUATION

WORD PROBLEM

There are 7 tricycles.

Each has 3 wheels.

How many wheels are there in all?

FIGURING

Home Note: Your child writes and solves a multiplication equation for a word problem.

Wheel Problems

DIRECTIONS

1

There are 5 bikes.

Each has 2 wheels.

How many wheels are there in all?

Read the word problem.

2

$5 \times 2 = \boxed{}$

Write the multiplication equation.

3

2, 4, 6, 8, 10

Show your figuring.

4

$5 \times 2 = \boxed{10}$

Write the answer.

---

①

EQUATION

WORD PROBLEM

There are 5 monster trucks.

Each has 4 wheels.

How many wheels are there in all?

FIGURING

②

EQUATION

WORD PROBLEM

There are 6 bikes.

Each has 2 wheels.

How many wheels are there in all?

FIGURING

Home Note: Your child writes and solves a multiplication equation for a word problem.

Lesson 12

21

Multiplication Word Problems

DIRECTIONS

1

$3 \times 2 = \boxed{}$

Read the multiplication equation.

2

There are (3 bikes).

Each has (2 wheels).

How many (wheels) are there in all?

Write a word problem.

3

(2, 4, 6)

Show your figuring.

4

$3 \times 2 = \boxed{6}$

Write the answer in the box.

---

① EQUATION

$2 \times 6 = \boxed{}$

WORD PROBLEM

There are _____.

Each has _____.

How many _____ are there in all?

FIGURING

---

② EQUATION

$5 \times 4 = \boxed{}$

WORD PROBLEM

There are _____.

Each has _____.

How many _____ are there in all?

FIGURING

Home Note: Your child writes a word problem for a given multiplication equation, and solves the equation.

Multiplication Word Problems

DIRECTIONS

- ➤ Read the multiplication equation.
- ➤ Write a word problem.
- ➤ Show your figuring.
- ➤ Write the answer in the box.

1

EQUATION

$6 \times 4 =$ ☐

WORD PROBLEM

There are _____.

Each has _____.

How many _____ are there in all?

FIGURING

2

EQUATION

$5 \times 5 =$ ☐

WORD PROBLEM

There are _____.

Each has _____.

How many _____ are there in all?

FIGURING

Home Note: Your child writes a word problem for a given multiplication equation, and solves the equation.

Multiplication Word Problems

DIRECTIONS

➤ Read the multiplication equation.
➤ Write a word problem.
➤ Show your figuring.
➤ Write the answer in the box.

1 EQUATION

$3 \times 4 =$ ☐

WORD PROBLEM

There are _____.

Each has _____.

How many _____ are there in all?

FIGURING

2 EQUATION

$4 \times 3 =$ ☐

WORD PROBLEM

There are _____.

Each has _____.

How many _____ are there in all?

FIGURING

Lesson 14

Home Note: Your child writes a word problem for a given multiplication equation, and solves the equation.

Show What You Know

DIRECTIONS

➤ Read the multiplication equation.

➤ Write a word problem.

➤ Show your figuring.

➤ Write the answer in the box.

1

EQUATION

$4 \times 4 = \boxed{}$

WORD PROBLEM

There are _____.

Each has _____.

How many _____ are there in all?

FIGURING

2

EQUATION

$6 \times 3 = \boxed{}$

WORD PROBLEM

There are _____.

Each has _____.

How many _____ are there in all?

FIGURING

Home Note: Your child writes a word problem for a given multiplication equation, and solves the equation.

Lesson 15

25

Show What You Know

DIRECTIONS

➤ Read the multiplication equation.
➤ Write a word problem.
➤ Show your figuring.
➤ Write the answer in the box.

1 **EQUATION**

$6 \times 5 = \boxed{}$

WORD PROBLEM

There are _____.

Each has _____.

How many _____ are there in all?

FIGURING

2 **EQUATION**

$5 \times 6 = \boxed{}$

WORD PROBLEM

There are _____.

Each has _____.

How many _____ are there in all?

FIGURING

Home Note: Your child writes a word problem for a given multiplication equation, and solves the equation.

Show What You Know

DIRECTIONS

➤ Read the multiplication equation.

➤ Write a word problem.

➤ Show your figuring.

➤ Write the answer in the box.

1

EQUATION

$5 \times 3 = \boxed{}$

WORD PROBLEM

There are _____.

Each has _____.

How many _____ are there in all?

FIGURING

2

EQUATION

$4 \times 2 = \boxed{}$

WORD PROBLEM

There are _____.

Each has _____.

How many _____ are there in all?

FIGURING

Home Note: Your child writes a word problem for a given multiplication equation, and solves the equation.

Number Cube Products

DIRECTIONS

➤ **Complete.**

$1 \times 1 =$ (1)

$1 \times 1 =$ _____

$1 \times 2 =$ _____

$1 \times 3 =$ _____

$1 \times 4 =$ _____

$1 \times 5 =$ _____

$1 \times 6 =$ _____

$2 \times 1 =$ _____

$2 \times 2 =$ _____

$2 \times 3 =$ _____

$2 \times 4 =$ _____

$2 \times 5 =$ _____

$2 \times 6 =$ _____

$3 \times 1 =$ _____

$3 \times 2 =$ _____

$3 \times 3 =$ _____

$3 \times 4 =$ _____

$3 \times 5 =$ _____

$3 \times 6 =$ _____

$4 \times 1 =$ _____

$4 \times 2 =$ _____

$4 \times 3 =$ _____

$4 \times 4 =$ _____

$4 \times 5 =$ _____

$4 \times 6 =$ _____

$5 \times 1 =$ _____

$5 \times 2 =$ _____

$5 \times 3 =$ _____

$5 \times 4 =$ _____

$5 \times 5 =$ _____

$5 \times 6 =$ _____

$6 \times 1 =$ _____

$6 \times 2 =$ _____

$6 \times 3 =$ _____

$6 \times 4 =$ _____

$6 \times 5 =$ _____

$6 \times 6 =$ _____

Home Note: Your child calculates products with factors 1 through 6.

Number Cube Products

➤ **Complete.**

(1) What is the greatest product for the factors 1 to 6? _____

(2) What is the least product for the factors 1 to 6? _____

(3) Which numbers from 1 to 36 are possible products from rolling two number cubes?
Circle them.

1	2	3	4	5	6
7	8	9	10	11	12
13	14	15	16	17	18
19	20	21	22	23	24
25	26	27	28	29	30
31	32	33	34	35	36

(4) Which products can be made from only one roll of two number cubes?

_____

(5) Which products can be made from two different rolls of two number cubes?

_____

(6) Which products can be made from more than two rolls of two number cubes?

_____

Home Note: Your child finds the possible products
of numbers rolled with two number cubes.

Multiplication Bingo

DIRECTIONS

1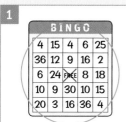
Write products in every square.

2
$2 \times 5 = 10$
Write the multiplication equation.

3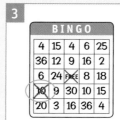
Mark out the product.

4
Bingo!
5 in a line wins.

BINGO

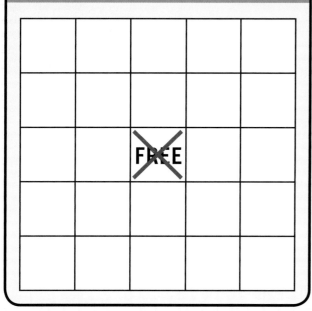

MULTIPLICATION EQUATIONS

Home Note: Your child plays *Bingo* to practice multiplication facts from 1 × 1 through 6 × 6.

Multiplication Bingo

➤ Write products in every square.

➤ Write the multiplication equation.

➤ Mark out the product.

➤ 5 in a line wins.

MULTIPLICATION EQUATIONS

Home Note: Your child plays *Bingo* to practice multiplication facts from 1 × 1 through 6 × 6.

Groups of Zero

DIRECTIONS

➤ Write the products.

➤ Write an addition equation for each multiplication equation.

① $1 \times 0 = $ ☐

② $2 \times 0 = $ ☐ _____

③ $3 \times 0 = $ ☐ _____

④ $4 \times 0 = $ ☐ _____

⑤ $5 \times 0 = $ ☐ _____

⑥ $6 \times 0 = $ ☐ _____

➤ Answer the questions.

⑦ Any number times zero equals _____.

   Why? _____

⑧ What products from page 28 should not be on a *Multiplication Bingo* card when

   the cubes will be 0–5 and 1–6? _____

   Why? _____

⑨ What products can you write on a *Multiplication Bingo* card when the cubes

   will be 0–5 and 1–6? _____

Home Note: Your child finds how rolling a number cube with a zero will affect the products in the *Bingo* game.

Multiplication Bingo with Zeros

DIRECTIONS

1 Write products in every square.

2 Write the multiplication equation.

$0 \times 5 = 0$

3 Mark out the product.

4 Bingo!

5 in a line wins.

BINGO

		~~FREE~~		

MULTIPLICATION EQUATIONS

_____ _____

_____ _____

_____ _____

_____ _____

_____ _____

_____ _____

_____ _____

_____ _____

_____ _____

_____ _____

_____ _____

Home Note: Your child plays *Bingo* to practice multiplication facts from 1×0 through 6×5.

Multiplication Bingo with Zeros

HOW TO PLAY

➤ Write products in every square.

➤ Write the multiplication equation.

➤ Mark out the product.

➤ 5 in a line wins.

MULTIPLICATION EQUATIONS

Lesson 18

Home Note: Your child plays *Bingo* to practice multiplication facts from 1×0 through 6×5.

Where the Lines Cross Practice

1

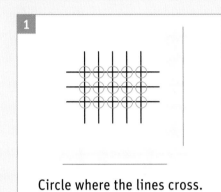

Circle where the lines cross.

2

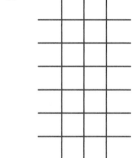

$3 \times 5 = 15$

Write the multiplication equation.

---

①

②

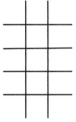

③

④

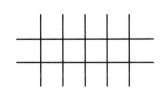

⑤

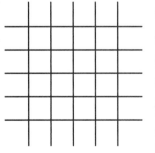

⑥

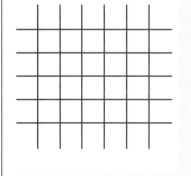

Home Note: Your child writes multiplication equations to match drawings.

Where the Lines Cross Practice

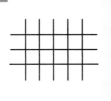
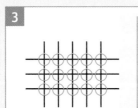
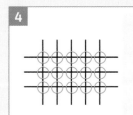

1

Roll the number cube. Draw that many lines across.

2

Roll the number cube again. Draw that many lines up and down.

3

Circle where the lines cross.

4

$3 \times 5 = 15$

Write the multiplication equation.

①

②

③

④

⑤

⑥

Lesson 19

Home Note: Your child draws models for multiplication and writes equations to match.

Game Rules for Where the Lines Cross

What you need

- number cube (1–6)
- *WorkSpace* page 38 or blank paper
- pencil

➤ **Players take turns. Each turn has four steps.**

1

Roll the number cube.
Draw that many lines across.

2

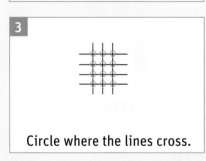

Roll the number cube again.
Draw that many lines
up and down.

3

Circle where the lines cross.

4

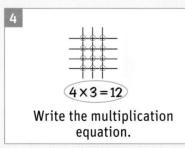

$$4 \times 3 = 12$$

Write the multiplication
equation.

➤ **The winner is the player who has the most
crossing points after six turns.**

Home Note: Your child plays a game, drawing models
for multiplication and writing equations to match.

Where the Lines Cross

HOW TO PLAY

➤ **Players take turns. Each turn has four steps.**

1 	**2** 	**3** 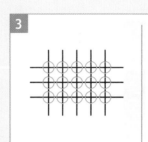	**4** 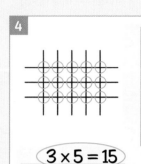
Roll the number cube. Draw that many lines across.	Roll the number cube again. Draw that many lines up and down.	Circle where the lines cross.	$3 \times 5 = 15$ Write the multiplication equation.

➤ **The winner is the player who has the most crossing points after six turns.**

①	②	③
④	**⑤**	**⑥**

Lesson 19

Home Note: Your child plays a game, drawing models for multiplication and writing equations to match.

Show What You Know

DIRECTIONS

➤ Write the product.

① 0 × 4 = ☐   ⑤ 6 × 0 = ☐   ⑨ 6 × 5 = ☐

② 3 × 5 = ☐   ⑥ 3 × 6 = ☐   ⑩ 3 × 4 = ☐

③ 6 × 3 = ☐   ⑦ 4 × 4 = ☐   ⑪ 4 × 6 = ☐

④ 3 × 1 = ☐   ⑧ 5 × 2 = ☐   ⑫ 3 × 3 = ☐

➤ Write one of the equations from above in the EQUATION box.

➤ Underline the product.

➤ Circle the factors.

➤ Show two different ways to figure.

⑬ **EQUATION**

⑭ **FIGURING**

Home Note: Your child solves a multiplication equation and explains how to solve a multiplication problem.

Game Rules for Multiplication Capture

What you need

- *Multiplication Capture* cards, 9 for each player, facedown in a pile
- *WorkSpace* page 41, 42, or blank paper
- pencil

➤ **Each turn has three steps.**

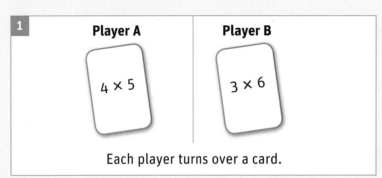

1. **Player A** 4×5 **Player B** 3×6

Each player turns over a card.

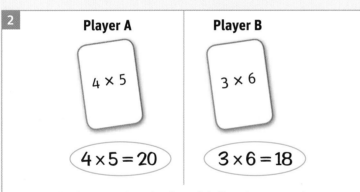

2. **Player A** 4×5 $4 \times 5 = 20$ **Player B** 3×6 $3 \times 6 = 18$

Each player writes both multiplication equations.

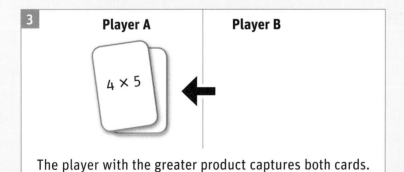

3. **Player A** 4×5 **Player B**

The player with the greater product captures both cards.

➤ **When all the cards have been played, the winner is the player who has the most cards.**

Lesson 20   **Home Note:** Your child plays a game that provides multiplication fact practice.

Multiplication Capture

HOW TO PLAY

1 | Player A | Player B

Start with 9 cards each.
Place them facedown in a pile.

2 | Player A | Player B

3×1 | 1×2

$3 \times 1 = 3$ $1 \times 2 = 2$

Players turn over one card
each, and write the
multiplication equations.

3 | Player A | Player B

3×1

The player with the greater
product captures both cards.

Player A	Player B

Home Note: Your child plays a game that
provides multiplication fact practice.

Lesson 20   **41**

Multiplication Capture

HOW TO PLAY

1

Player A	Player B

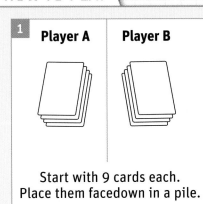

Start with 9 cards each.
Place them facedown in a pile.

2

Player A	Player B

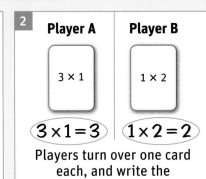

3 × 1 = 3   1 × 2 = 2

Players turn over one card
each, and write the
multiplication equations.

3

Player A	Player B

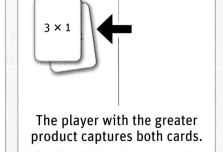

The player with the greater
product captures both cards.

Player A	Player B

Home Note: Your child plays a game that
provides multiplication fact practice.

Which Has More Tiles?

1

$\underline{3}$ rows with

$\underline{2}$ tiles in each row.

Complete the descriptions.

2

$2 + 2 + 2 = 6$

$2, 4, 6$

Three groups of two equals six

Use numbers, words, and pictures to show at least two different ways to figure the products.

3

$\underline{3}$ rows with

$\underline{2}$ tiles in each row.

$3 \times 2 = 6$

Write the equation.

4

$3 \times 2 = 6$

$3 \times 1 = 3$

Circle the equation for more tiles.

_____ rows with

_____ tiles in each row

_____ rows with

_____ tiles in each row

FIGURING

Home Note: Your child represents tile arrangements with words and multiplication equations, figures the products in two ways, and compares products to decide which is greater.

Which Has More Tiles?

DIRECTIONS

➤ Complete the descriptions.

➤ Use numbers, words, and pictures to show at least two different ways to figure the products.

➤ Write the equation.

➤ Circle the equation for more tiles.

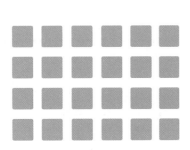

_____ rows with

_____ tiles in each row

_____ rows with

_____ tiles in each row

FIGURING

 Home Note: Your child represents tile arrangements with words and multiplication equations, figures the products in two ways, and compares products to decide which is greater.

Where the Lines Cross

1

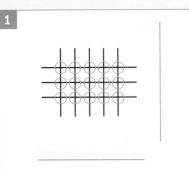

Circle where the lines cross.

2

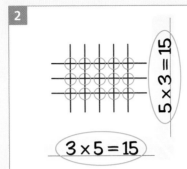

$3 \times 5 = 15$

$5 \times 3 = 15$

Write multiplication equations.

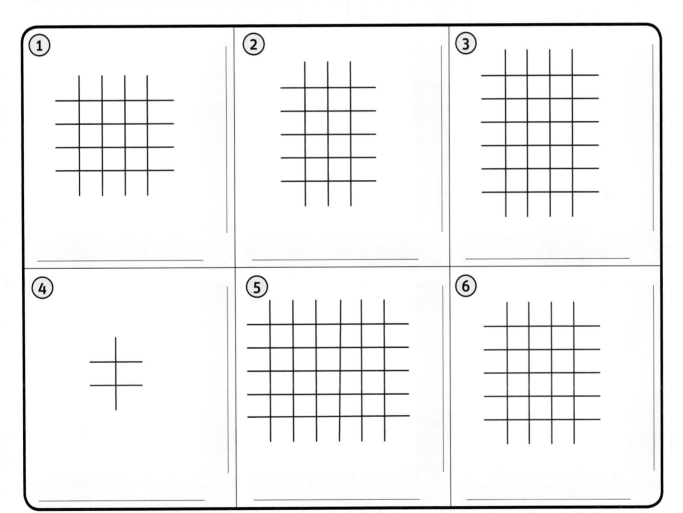

Home Note: Your child writes related multiplication equations to represent a picture, demonstrating that factors in any order produce the same product.

Lesson 22

45

Game Rules for Where the Lines Cross Capture

What you need

- *Where the Lines Cross Capture* cards, 9 for each player
- *WorkSpace* page 47 or blank paper
- pencil

➤ **Each turn has three steps.**

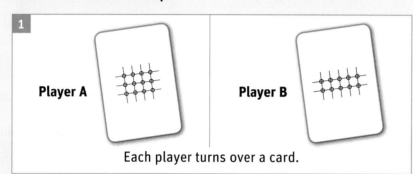

1

Player A   **Player B**

Each player turns over a card.

2

Player A   **Player B**

$3 \times 4 = 12$
$4 \times 3 = 12$

$2 \times 5 = 10$
$5 \times 2 = 10$

Each player writes both multiplication equations for each card.

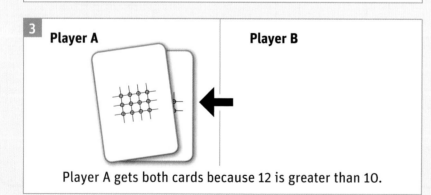

3   **Player A**   **Player B**

Player A gets both cards because 12 is greater than 10.

➤ **When all the cards have been played, the player who has the most cards is the winner.**

Home Note: Your child plays a game, writing equations to match models for multiplication.

Where the Lines Cross Capture

HOW TO PLAY

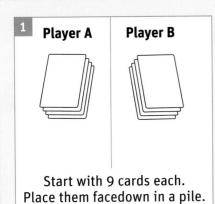

1 | Player A | Player B

Start with 9 cards each.
Place them facedown in a pile.

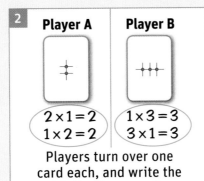

2 | Player A | Player B

$$2 \times 1 = 2$$
$$1 \times 2 = 2$$

$$1 \times 3 = 3$$
$$3 \times 1 = 3$$

Players turn over one card each, and write the multiplication equations.

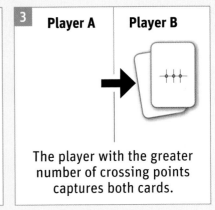

3 | Player A | Player B

The player with the greater number of crossing points captures both cards.

Player A	Player B

Home Note: Your child plays a game, writing equations to match models for multiplication.

Multiplication

➤ Tell about multiplication with words, numbers, and pictures.

ABOUT MULTIPLICATION

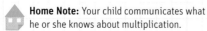

Home Note: Your child communicates what he or she knows about multiplication.

Game Rules for Tiles Capture

What you need

- *Tiles Capture* cards, 9 for each player
- *WorkSpace* page 50 or blank paper
- pencil

➤ **Each turn has three steps.**

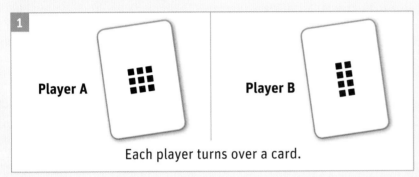

1

Player A   Player B

Each player turns over a card.

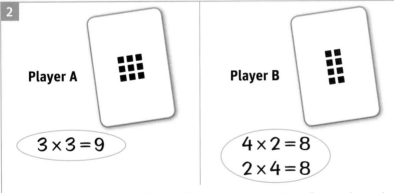

2

Player A $3 \times 3 = 9$

Player B $4 \times 2 = 8$
            $2 \times 4 = 8$

Each player writes both multiplication equations for each card.

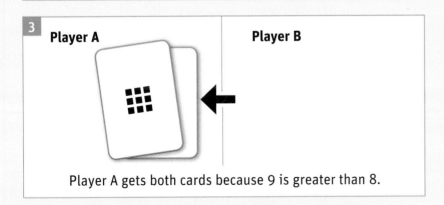

3

Player A   Player B

Player A gets both cards because 9 is greater than 8.

➤ **When all the cards have been played, the player who has the most cards is the winner.**

Home Note: Your child plays a game, writing equations to match models for multiplication.

Lesson 24

49

Tiles Capture

1 | Player A | Player B

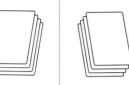

Start with 9 cards each. Place them facedown in a pile.

2 | Player A | Player B

$2 \times 1 = 2$
$1 \times 2 = 2$

$3 \times 1 = 3$
$1 \times 3 = 3$

Players turn over one card each, and write the multiplication equations.

3 | Player A | Player B

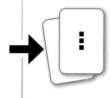

The player with the greater number of tiles captures both cards.

Player A	Player B

50 Lesson 24

Home Note: Your child plays a game, writing equations to match models for multiplication.

Multiplication Capture

1 Player A   Player B

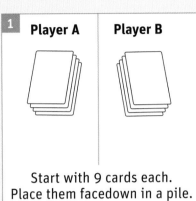

Start with 9 cards each.
Place them facedown in a pile.

2 Player A   Player B

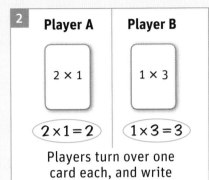

2×1 1×3

$2 \times 1 = 2$ $1 \times 3 = 3$

Players turn over one
card each, and write
multiplication equations.

3 Player A   Player B

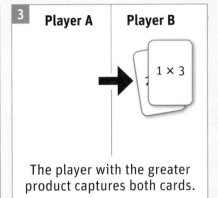

1×3

The player with the greater
product captures both cards.

Player A	Player B

Home Note: Your child plays a game,
completing multiplication equations.

Show What You Know

DIRECTIONS

➤ Write the product.

① $0 \times 4 =$ ☐

② $4 \times 5 =$ ☐

③ $2 \times 6 =$ ☐

④ $3 \times 5 =$ ☐

⑤ $2 \times 2 =$ ☐

⑥ $3 \times 3 =$ ☐

⑦ $6 \times 6 =$ ☐

⑧ $3 \times 6 =$ ☐

⑨ $6 \times 5 =$ ☐

⑩ $4 \times 4 =$ ☐

⑪ $5 \times 2 =$ ☐

⑫ $6 \times 4 =$ ☐

⑬ $3 \times 4 =$ ☐

⑭ $2 \times 0 =$ ☐

⑮ $1 \times 6 =$ ☐

⑯ $2 \times 4 =$ ☐

⑰ $5 \times 5 =$ ☐

⑱ $5 \times 1 =$ ☐

⑲ $3 \times 2 =$ ☐

⑳ $6 \times 3 =$ ☐

㉑ $5 \times 4 =$ ☐

➤ Write one of the equations from above in the EQUATION box.

➤ Draw a line under the product.

➤ Circle the factors.

➤ Use numbers, words, and pictures to show two different ways to figure.

㉒ **EQUATION**

㉓ **FIGURING**

Home Note: Your child completes multiplication equations and explains how to solve a multiplication problem.

Show What You Know

➤ Write both multiplication equations that match the picture.

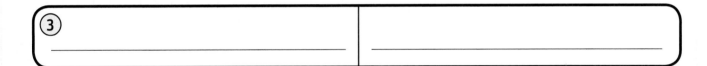

① _____

_____

② _____

_____

➤ Write two equations to show the Commutative Property of Multiplication.

③ _____   _____

➤ Use numbers, pictures, and the words *factor* and *product* to tell about the Commutative Property of Multiplication.

④

Home Note: Your child writes two equations that are examples of the Commutative Property of Multiplication and explains what the Commutative Property of Multiplication is.

Word Problems

1

There are (3 bikes).

Each has (2 wheels).

How many (wheels) are there in all?

Write a word problem.

2

$3 \times 2 = \square$

Write the equation.

3

$2, 4, 6$

$2 + 2 + 2 = 6$

Figure two ways.

4

$3 \times 2 = 6$

Solve the equation.

---

1 EQUATION

WORD PROBLEM

There are _____.

Each has _____.

How many _____ are there in all?

FIGURING

---

2 EQUATION

WORD PROBLEM

There are _____.

Each has _____.

How many _____ are there in all?

FIGURING

Home Note: Your child writes word problems and the matching equations, and shows two ways of figuring the solutions.

Billy Wins a Shopping Spree

➤ Billy has won a Science Museum Store gift certificate. He is going to go on a shopping spree at the store. Billy can choose any items he wants, as long as they don't cost more than $25 in all.

SCIENCE MUSEUM STORE PRICES

$3

Origami paper

Magnet

Stuffed gecko

Prism

$4

Kaleidoscope

Bug box

Scrapbook kit

Inflatable shark

$5

Juggling balls

Glow-in-the-dark stars

Inflatable globe

Model dinosaur kit

Home Note: Your child uses this price list to solve a problem with multiplication, addition, and subtraction. The problem has many possible correct answers.

Museum Store Receipt

DIRECTIONS

1

. Choose items from the Science Museum Store price list.

2

WRITE WHAT YOU CHOOSE

$3

| Origami paper | 1 |
| Magnet | 1 |

Write what you choose.

3

SCIENCE MUSEUM RECEIPT

2 items for $3 each

1 items for $4 each

Complete the receipt.

WRITE WHAT YOU CHOOSE

$3

Origami paper	_____
Magnet	_____
Stuffed gecko	_____
Prism	_____

$4

Kaleidoscope	_____
Bug box	_____
Scrapbook kit	_____
Inflatable shark	_____

$5

Juggling balls	_____
Glow-in-the-dark stars	_____
Inflatable globe	_____
Model dinosaur kit	_____

SCIENCE MUSEUM RECEIPT

_____ items for $3 each $ _____ in all

_____ items for $4 each $ _____ in all

_____ items for $5 each $ _____ in all

TOTAL $ _____

Money left over $ _____

Home Note: Your child solves a problem with multiplication, addition, and subtraction. The problem has many possible correct answers.

Spending Exactly $25 at the Museum Store

DIRECTIONS

➤ Find a combination of items that have a total price of $25.

➤ Complete the receipt.

1

SCIENCE MUSEUM RECEIPT

_____ items for $3 each $ _____ in all

_____ items for $4 each $ _____ in all

_____ items for $5 each $ _____ in all

                              TOTAL $_____

2

SCIENCE MUSEUM RECEIPT

_____ items for $3 each $ _____ in all

_____ items for $4 each $ _____ in all

_____ items for $5 each $ _____ in all

                              TOTAL $_____

Home Note: Your child solves a problem with multiplication and addition. The problem has many possible correct answers.

Show What You Know

DIRECTIONS

➤ Write the product.

① 4 × 5 = ☐   ⑥ 2 × 3 = ☐   ⑪ 7 × 2 = ☐

② 3 × 0 = ☐   ⑦ 6 × 6 = ☐   ⑫ 4 × 1 = ☐

③ 1 × 6 = ☐   ⑧ 1 × 0 = ☐   ⑬ 3 × 6 = ☐

④ 3 × 5 = ☐   ⑨ 6 × 5 = ☐   ⑭ 5 × 5 = ☐

⑤ 6 × 4 = ☐   ⑩ 4 × 3 = ☐   ⑮ 0 × 5 = ☐

➤ Write one of the equations from above in the EQUATION box.

➤ Draw a line under the product.

➤ Circle the factors.

➤ Use numbers, words, and pictures to show two different ways to figure.

⑯ **EQUATION**

⑰ **FIGURING**

Home Note: Your child completes multiplication equations and explains how to solve a multiplication problem.

Word Problems

DIRECTIONS

➤ Read the word problem or equation.

➤ Figure two ways.

➤ Solve the equation.

1 **EQUATION**

WORD PROBLEM

There are 4 beetles.

Each has 6 legs.

How many legs are there in all?

FIGURING

2 **EQUATION**

$$6 \times 3 = \boxed{}$$

WORD PROBLEM

There are _____.

Each has _____.

How many _____ are there in all?

FIGURING

Home Note: Your child writes and solves a multiplication equation for a word problem, and writes a word problem to match a multiplication equation.

Show What You Know

➤ Write two equations that show the Commutative Property of Multiplication.

① EQUATIONS

_____   _____

➤ Write at least three sentences about multiplication.

➤ Use the words *factor*, *product*, *equal groups*, and *addition*.

② ABOUT MULTIPLICATION

Lesson 30

Home Note: Your child writes about multiplication and provides an example of the Commutative Property of Multiplication.

Math Vocabulary

 Home Note: Your child records terms and examples of math vocabulary.

Math Vocabulary

Math Vocabulary

Home Note: Your child records terms and examples of math vocabulary.

Glossary

addition equation

An *addition equation* is a number sentence with an equal sign to show that two amounts have the same value. There is addition on one or both sides of the equal sign. For example, $12 = 3 + 3 + 3 + 3$.

Commutative Property of Multiplication

Changing the order of factors does not change the product. This is called the *Commutative Property of Multiplication*. An example of this property is $3 \times 5 = 5 \times 3$.

equal

Equal means the same amount. For example, twelve is *equal* to three times four. The symbol for *equal* is $=$.

equal groups

In *equal groups*, each group has the same amount. For example, if there are circles and each circle has 2 stars, then the stars are in equal groups.

equation

An *equation* is a number sentence that uses an equal sign to show that two amounts have the same value. For example, $3 + 4 = 7$, $3 \times 4 = 12$, $5 - 0 = 5$ are *equations*.

factor

Factors are numbers that you multiply to get a product. For example, 3 and 7 are *factors* in the equation $3 \times 7 = 21$.

multiplication

Multiplication is what you do when you find the total number of items in equal groups.

multiplication equation

A *multiplication equation* is a number sentence with an equal sign and a times sign. What is on the left side of the equal sign equals what is on the right side. Examples of *multiplication equations* are $18 = 6 \times 3$ and $6 \times 3 = 18$.

Multiplication Property of One

The product of any number and 1 is the number. For example, 7×1 and 1×7 both equal 7.

multiply

Multiply is what you do when you find the product of factors. For example, if you *multiply* 5 and 2, you get the product 10.

plus

The word *plus* tells you to add. 3 plus 3 means you should add 3 and 3. The symbol for *plus* is $+$.

Glossary

product

A *product* is the answer you get when you multiply. For example, 21 is the *product* in the equation $7 \times 3 = 21$.

symbols

You use *symbols* in mathematics to name numbers (12, 308, $\frac{1}{2}$), operations ($+$, $-$, $\times$, $\div$), and relationships between numbers ($=$, $>$, $<$).

times

The word *times* tells you to multiply. Four *times* two means you should combine four groups of two. The symbol for *times* is $\times$.

Zero Property of Multiplication

The product of any number and zero is zero. For example, 0×7 and 7×0 both equal 0.